Colorful
Chickens and Roosters

Coloring Book for Adults

CREATIVE COLORING PRESS

BONUS PAGES

DRAGON
COLORING BOOK FOR ADULTS

INCLUDES 38 DAZZLING DRAGON DESIGNS TO COLOR

Dragon Coloring Book for Adults by Creative Coloring Press
Available now at Amazon.com, Barnes and Noble, and other online retailers.

Elephant Coloring Book for Adults by Creative Coloring Press
Available now at Amazon.com, Barnes and Noble, and other online retailers.

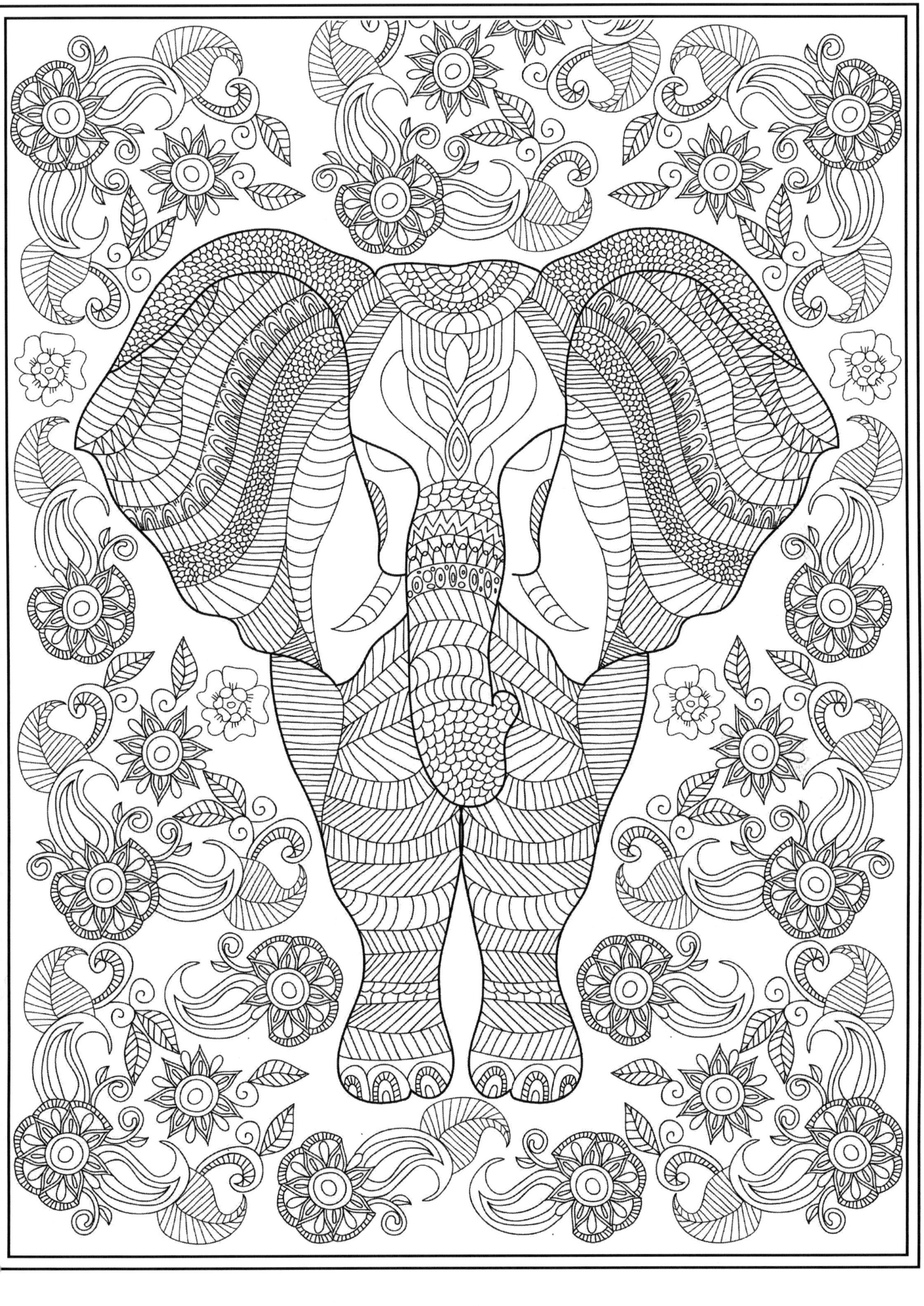

CREATIVE COLORING PRESS

LIFE UNDER THE SEA

COLORING BOOK FOR ADULTS

An Ocean Coloring Adventure

Life Under the Sea Coloring Book for Adults by Creative Coloring Press
Available now at Amazon.com, Barnes and Noble, and other online retailers.

COLORFUL CITIES

FUN AND FANCIFUL BUILDINGS AND URBAN DESIGNS

A COLORING BOOK FOR GROWN-UPS

ALISA CALDER

Colorful Cities: Fun and Fanciful Urban Designs by Alisa Calder.
Available now at Amazon.com, Barnes and Noble, and other online retailers.

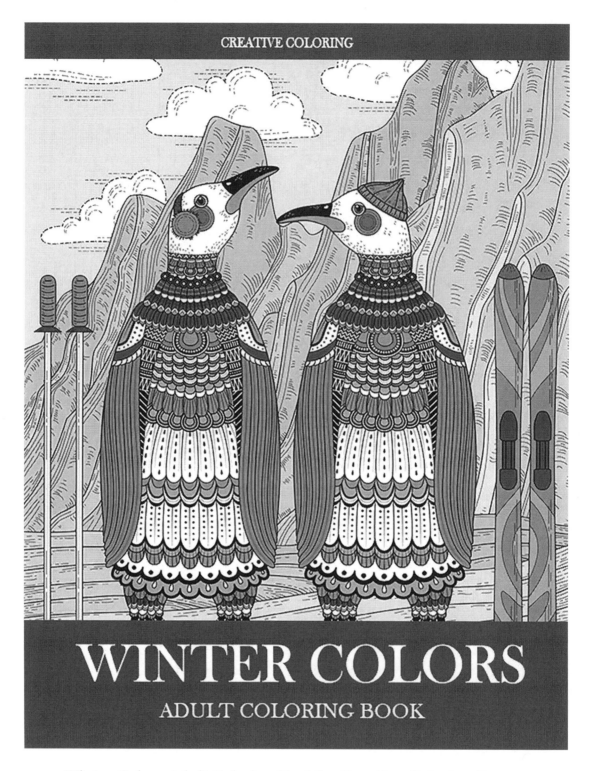

WINTER COLORS

ADULT COLORING BOOK

Winter Colors Adult Coloring Book by Creative Coloring Press.
Available now at Amazon.com, Barnes and Noble, and other online retailers.

Made in the USA
Las Vegas, NV
20 January 2021